A copy of this book is available from the British Library

ISBN: 978-1-8381619-0-3

First published 2020

This book is dedicated to my two heavenly babies, Anna and Caidain who taught me to live a richer more meaningful life and that love endures beyond this life. Your lives touched this world in beautiful ways, one of which is by inspiring me to write this book.

This book is also dedicated to all the children who didn't get to meet their brother or sister.

All monies raised by the sale of this book will go towards supporting families bereaved by pregnancy loss.

Thank you for purchasing this book.

Acknowledgements

I want to thank a number of people who were involved in our journey of pregnancy losses and who made this book possible.

Thank you to all the staff in maternity services in South West Acute Hospital, Enniskillen and Altnagelvin Hospital, Derry, Northern Ireland for their sensitive care, understanding and dedication to their role.

A special thanks to Ann O'Reilly, an amazing midwife and friend who has recently retired.

Thanks especially to Melissa Crochett, Bereavement midwife with the Western Health and Social Care Trust in Northern Ireland who really does go above and beyond her role in providing care to those who have received devastating news. You were such a much needed source of comfort, reassurance, knowledge and guidance in our time of utter sorrow and despair.

Thanks to Dr. Bailie and her team from Fetal Medicine in the Royal Victoria Hospital, Belfast. Thanks for your sensitive care and expertise.

Thank you to Hannah Mc Keown working on behalf of Remember my Baby, who came to the hospital and took photographs.

Thanks to Mary Mc Donald, from the Northern Ireland Childrens Hospice, who helped us make the family tree and who supported us as a family before and after I had Caidain.

Thanks to all my family and friends, who got me through the very dark days, I am blessed to have you all in my life.

Thanks to everyone who donated to get this book ready for publishing.

Thank you to Aideen Mc Ginley, one of life's great supporters, who believed in this book from the very start.

Thank you to Gráinne Knox an amazing talented artist and illustrator, who brought to life our story in the most heartfelt way.

To my husband Andrew, thank you for always being there for me, I wouldn't be the person I am today if it wasn't for you.

To my children, Erin-Rose and Andrew, thank you, you both were the reason I wanted to write this book, it's a privilege to be your Mummy.

Preface

The idea for this book was inspired by the death of our 2 babies, Anna who was stillborn at 18 weeks in 2017 and Caidain who was stillborn at 33 weeks gestation in 2019. We had 2 children who were very aware of the pregnancies and we struggled to find appropriate resources to help explain the loss in a child friendly way. I work as a Clinical Psychologist and think stories are a fantastic resource for children with many benefits.

During my pregnancy with Caidain, we knew at around 23 weeks that Caidain was not going to survive. He was diagnosed with Edwards' Syndrome which is a severe chromosomal disorder. Anna was diagnosed with Down's Syndrome at about 16 weeks gestation.

As parents, we wanted to protect our children from this horrific news but knew that we couldn't and that added to our pain. We were reeling from the news and worried about how and when to tell them and how they would react. Like us, they were very excited and looking forward to meeting the baby.

There was a period when we as parents knew our baby wouldn't survive but didn't feel ready to tell the children, however it was very painful to hear their excited hopes for when the baby comes and it just felt so wrong to continue with the silence.

We were so relieved when we told them. It felt like a great weight had been lifted. It enabled open, honest but difficult conversations about what would happen when the baby was born.

This story is our experience of losing Caidain and written through the eyes of our oldest daughter, Erin-Rose who was 8 years old at the time of diagnosis. Our story and contents may not be in keeping with your family's belief system. I appreciate that every family may deal with this experience differently

In writing this book, my sincerest hope is to bring a little comfort to this very painful experience. I also hope that it helps your child to know that other children have experienced similar and have had similar thoughts and feelings to them. I also wanted to bring hope, that after terrible tragedy, the intense feelings of grief lessen and they can still think of their brother or sister in spirit and remember them in special ways.

I believe as parents, you carry your child's grief as well as your own but understanding your child's grief and how they can be supported can make the load a little easier. I have included some suggestions at the end on this topic.

I hope you and your child find this book useful and supportive in helping with conversations about the very painful and tragic reality of pregnancy and early baby loss.

Hi my name is Erin-Rose, I am 8 and a half years old, this is a true story about something very sad that happened to our family.

This is my family, my Mum, Dad and younger brother, Andrew

Last year, my Mummy was growing a
baby in her tummy, she was
pregnant. We were very excited to
meet our new little brother or sister.
Me and my brother talked about
what we would do to help when the
baby comes, like bringing the baby
for walks, changing their nappy
(eww!) and giving the baby a bottle.

Me and my brother used to kiss my Mummy's
tummy before we left for school.

Then one day things changed. A very sad thing happened. The doctor gave my Mum and Dad very sad news. They told them that the baby in my mummy's tummy is very sick.

The doctor told my mum and dad that they are very sorry but they could not make the baby well again. The baby's body did not grow properly and couldn't survive outside my mummy's tummy. The baby would probably die before it was born.

When Mum and Dad told us the sad news, I felt lots of big strong feelings. I felt so sad, shocked and mad. I wanted to know, why did this happen to us? What did we do wrong? I did not want this bad news to be true.

It wasn't fair. I was so mad that I wasn't going to be a big sister again. I worried that I had caused the baby to be sick in some way, like the time I accidently bumped into my Mummy's tummy. Inside, my heart felt very sore and heavy, I cried a lot.
Andrew didn't cry, he just looked really sad and hugged Mummy and Daddy.

I told Mum how I was feeling and she said that, "Everything you are feeling I am feeling too, its okay to feel that way. You didn't do anything to cause this, it is no one's fault.
Nothing you said or did or even thought has made the baby sick.
Sometimes babies don't get to be born healthy and die. It hurts very much that this has happened, I know how much you wanted to be a big sister again"

As time passed, when I got these strong feelings of sadness, anger or had worries, I would tell my Mum or Dad. Sometimes I would draw pictures.

Sometimes I would go out and bounce on the trampoline in the garden with Andrew. Andrew told me he wished that the baby would survive and we would still get to have a brother or sister.

A nice lady came to our home and helped us make a picture of a family tree. Everyone in our family put one hand in paint and made handprints for the leaves. She said that when the baby is born we need to get their handprint on the tree too.

After a few months, it was time for the baby to be born. My Mummy and Daddy went to the hospital for a few days. I reminded Mummy to take the family tree we made and to get the baby's hand prints. I was scared when my Mummy went into hospital and was afraid that she might die.

My Auntie Una and Auntie Yvonne looked after us for a few days and I talked to Mum and Dad every day on the phone. I felt better after I talked to Mum and Dad.

In hospital, my Mummy had a baby boy, but he died. We didn't visit Mummy and the baby in hospital. My Mummy named our baby brother who had died, Cadain, which means 'fighter .'

When Mummy and Daddy came home from hospital, they brought our little brother Caidain home too. He was wrapped in a blanket and we put him in a special cot.

Even though Caidain had died, we still got to hold him. He just looked like a baby sleeping. Andrew held him first, I was a bit scared and didn't hold him until the next day. I was afraid of hurting him but Daddy said that when someone dies their body doesn't work, their body doesn't feel anything anymore and they don't feel pain at all.

Mum and Dad took photographs of us holding him. It felt a bit weird and awkward at the time but now I am glad we have photographs of us together. We added his hand print to our family tree picture.

The Teague family

All our family, my Aunties, Uncles, Grandparents and Cousins came to meet him too. Everyone was very sad and cried when they saw him lying in the cot.
That night I heard Mummy and Andrew laughing when she was reading Andrew a bedtime story, Andrew had told her, 'I am sorry to tell you this Mummy but the baby looks like an alien!' Mummy explained that Caidain's skin had wrinkled with the heat.

The day after Mum and Dad brought Caidain home from the hospital, we had a funeral service in church for Caidain. A funeral service is when we say goodbye to the person who has died.

That evening at home, we put Caidain's body in a little white coffin. We had two teddies the same, we put one teddy beside him in the coffin and we kept one. We all kissed him Goodbye. It was very sad. I was crying inside.

At the funeral service, the Priest said prayers and two ladies sang songs. My Aunties and Mummy said readings and poems.

We put Caidain's coffin beside other babies who had died in the graveyard. Everyone looked very sad. Mummy, Daddy, me and Andrew put one white rose each on top of his coffin.

Even though we can't see Caidain anymore, we believe his spirit or soul left his body when he died and went to heaven. Daddy says we can think of him as an angel in heaven, happy and safe being looked after by our two Granddads who are in heaven too.

Shortly after Caidain died, I had lots of worries about other people in my family dying too. I felt stressed sometimes and did not want to be apart from my Mum and Dad. It helped to talk to my Mummy and Daddy. I sometimes got really mad and cried especially at night when me and Mummy talked.

Even though we didn't get to meet him alive, me and Andrew still miss our little brother and feel sad sometimes. As time passed, I still felt sad but not as much. We still talk about him and he is always part of our family. Mummy says we are always connected to Caidain by the love we have for him.

One day, a few weeks after Caidain died, my Mummy
told us that she was very sad and missed him very
much. She asked God for a sign that he was okay. A
few minutes later as she was driving in the car,
a rainbow appeared right in front of the car and stayed
there as she drove along for a few minutes.
We always look for rainbows now as they remind us
of Caidain.

I like it when we do things to remember Caidain. We have a memory box which has some clothes that he wore, his footprint and handprints, a small teddy and photographs of us together. We sometimes go to his grave especially on special occasions like Christmas and leave flowers. We sometimes light candles at home and pray for him. We also did some kind acts in Caidain's name like making a donation to a charity and buying some Christmas presents for children in his name. I really liked doing that.

Even though we had to say Goodbye before we even met, we will always love Caidain and think of him as our brother in heaven looking down on us and loving us too. He will always be part of our family.

Dear child,

I am so sorry if your Baby Brother or Sister died, before you got a chance to meet them or they died shortly after they were born. Sadly, this happens to other families too. When someone you love dies, it really hurts. Even if you didn't get to meet your Baby Brother or Sister, it can still hurt a lot. You were looking forward to being a Big Brother or Sister.

Sometimes babies who grow in our Mummies' tummies don't have a healthy body and can't survive outside our Mummies' tummies. Some babies have heart problems, some babies have lung problems so they cant breathe, some babies' organs don't grow properly. Your baby brother or sister that has died did not feel any pain when they died.

It is no one's fault that your brother or sister died. Nothing you said or did or thought caused it to happen. It is hard for us to understand why sad things happen sometimes.

It is okay to cry when you feel sad and its okay to get mad. This is a terrible, sad and painful event that has happened to you and your family. You might feel angry at God, the Doctors, your Parents or your other Brothers or Sisters. It might feel unfair that you didn't get to be a Big Brother or Sister. You might feel jealous of other children you know who have Baby Brothers or Sisters.

It is okay to ask questions and talk about the baby. Please talk to your parents or a trusted adult about any worries you have. Please don't be afraid that they will be upset if you ask questions. Even if your Mum and Dad get upset, they will be glad that you are asking questions.

You might think that other people in your family are going to die too, this is a very normal worry, but that is very unlikely to happen. Most people live a long life and there will always be people to take care of you.

You might have trouble sleeping or have sore tummy or head when you feel really sad.

Sometimes you might want more hugs and cuddles and be near people you love. Sometimes you might want to be alone and not talk about anything.

The sadness you feel will get better as time passes. It won't hurt so much inside. You might feel bad when you start to feel less sad or have times when you are happy, but this is all normal, your Brother or Sister who died would want you to feel happy and enjoy your life.

Doing things to remember your Brother or Sister who you didn't get to meet might help you feel better. You can remember them in lots of special ways. Writing a letter to them or drawing a picture, looking at photos, lighting a candle on special occasions or visiting their grave. Planting a tree or keeping a memory box are all really special ways to remember them.

The love you have for your Brother or Sister who has died will always be in your heart and I truly believe even though you didn't get to meet them, they still love you too.

Always remember you are loved, safe and very special.

I hope in time your heart will stop hurting so much and you will have many happy days.

Irene

For Parents

Dear parent,

If you are a parent who has experienced pregnancy loss, still birth or early child loss, I am so sorry that you have experienced this extremely painful and devastating experience.

These are just a few suggestions to help you support your children. Not all of them may be appropriate for your family.

As a parent, your instinct is to protect your children from the pain of loss but hiding it from them is also an added stress on you as parents.

Children will sense your pain and anguish no matter how hard you try to hide it. So even with young children it is best to be open and honest. I understand telling your child(ren) is an incredibly hard thing to do, especially when you are shocked and grieving yourself. You might find your childs' reactions surprise you, children can be incredibly resilient.

You might find that their hope, courage and wisdom will shine a light through these dark days.

Telling your child

If you don't feel like you can explain because you are so overwhelmed, its ok to ask another trusted familiar adult to explain what has happened. They could explain what has happened and that you are too sad to talk right now because the baby died and will talk to you soon.

• Starting with an honest, short explanation that the baby has died, the baby's gender and name. You might add that the baby's body wasn't strong enough to live outside Mummy's tummy or that the baby's body wasn't working properly.

• Children can tend to take things literally so try not to use phrases such as the baby went to 'sleep', or they are 'gone'. Children might be afraid to go to 'sleep' or think if the baby is 'gone' they could be found again and come back. These phrases can cause confusion and lead to anxiety.

• Explain that you are very sad and that's its ok to feel sad and cry when sad things happen.

• Reassure children that no one is to blame for the death of the baby. Some children may believe that something they said, did or thought caused the death of the baby.

• Keep the initial explanation short as children may get easily overwhelmed with too much talking. Children will tend to ask more questions in their own time, however they need to hear the message that it is ok to talk about the death of their sibling and it is ok to ask questions.

• Try and give short direct answers to questions and give the same response to repeat questions.

Involving Children

While I was pregnant, the bereavement midwife suggested that we take our dead baby home before we buried him, our first reaction was shock and worry about how our children would react and how it would affect them.

However, through discussion and encouragement, I am so glad we made the decision to bring him home. At the time, it felt natural and the right thing to do. It was so comforting to know that Caidain came home with us, it also allowed us to spend special family time together with him, holding him, sharing our grief with the wider family and taking precious treasured photographs.

• Involving children in the death/funeral rituals is also a good idea. It helps with their grief and helps them feel included and an important part of the family.

• Explaining what will happen at a funeral in advance so they know what to expect can help reduce anxiety. They also need to be told that people will be sad and might cry.

• Explaining that the baby's body does not work anymore and they don't feel anything is a good idea as they might be distressed at the baby going into a coffin.

• Depending on your child's age they could be involved in the service itself like picking some music or putting something in the coffin like a teddy, a picture or a letter.

• It also might help to have a relative close to the child who can support them so you can partake fully in the service.

• Some children may not want to go to the funeral or with very young children, you might decide not to have them at the funeral. Instead they could be involved at a memorial ritual, visiting a burial place or planting a tree.

Supporting your child

This is something that can, at times be very hard to do, especially when you are grieving yourself. Children can display intense emotions when grieving and need you or another adult to contain and soothe these emotional storms. Reassure your child that its ok to talk about or ask questions about the baby/death etc. Let them know if you get upset its because you are feeling sad. Maybe adding that crying is a good way to release sadness and painful feelings, as this may help them be more comfortable with their own and others expression of grief.

• Let your child know you understand they are having difficult feelings and these feelings are normal when people experience a loss.
• Help them recognise their grief and name the associated feelings. This can help with normalising and validating their feelings. It also helps them feel understood.
• The message that expression of emotion is better rather than keeping it bottled up is a useful one to convey to your child.
• If your child finds it hard to talk you might say something like, 'Some things are hard to talk about but talking things through can really help'.
• Sharing your own feelings and telling children you are sad for their loss too. It can help children accept their feelings if they know others feel the same.
• Giving the message that nothing they said, did or thought can cause death would be important even if they don't verbalise any guilt related feelings.
• As well as encouraging your child to talk about the death, encourage your child to draw a picture, write a story/letter/poem or act out the event with toys. Creative play can be a way for them to express their feelings. The more the child is able to safely tell the 'story' the more they can process the event.
• When dealing with strong emotions such as anger which may show up as aggression to others, its important to connect first with the emotion before we correct, for example, 'I understand you are angry and upset right now and you are having a hard time however, hitting your brother is not a good choice and we need to find other ways to help you calm down.'
• Some children may be upset at the disruption in routine that comes with a death in the family. Keeping a consistent routine and maintaining rules and expectations of behaviour will provide children with a sense of security and stability . Routine is comforting and reassuring to children, try and keep rituals such as the bedtime story.
• Letting others know that your child's baby brother or sister has died, such as childminders, teachers and other people who spend time with them is important in order for them to understand and respond to your child's grief reactions. Telling them what explanation has been given to your child also avoids any misunderstandings and ensures consistency.
• Most difficult grief related behaviours resolve with time, understanding and support. There are local and national bereavement support services which you may seek more specialised support from, some of which are listed in this book.
• Reading child bereavement books with children can also be a good way to open up difficult conversations or allow them to express unexpressed feelings and thoughts. Some of these are referenced later.
• It is extremely helpful and healing as a family to create special ways of remembering your baby. Memory boxes are great, it is a specific box that can be made or bought, in which to put treasured items such as items of clothing, photographs, hand prints, footprints. Visiting the grave, planting a tree, artwork and lighting candles are all ways to remember .

School/Nursery Support

• Inform all relevant school/nursery staff about your child's situation. This can help prevent unhelpful reactions to grief related behaviours and increase understanding and support. They could also help if your child is reluctant to return to school.
• It may be helpful to negotiate a contact person who would be available when they need time to talk.
• A suitable place in school/nursery may be allocated to take quiet time out if they need it.
• Ongoing contact may be maintained with school/nursery to check how they are coping while there.

How grief affects children

Grief can have a huge emotional, psychological and physical impact on children.

• Children tend to show their grief in many ways. Grief is different for every child and depending on their age , their understanding of death is different. Like adults, children of any age are likely to experience a range of feelings, including shock, fear, disbelief, anger, sadness, guilt and resentment.
• Depending on their age and developmental stage, children may not be able to verbalise their feelings and may instead express their distress through changes in their behaviour and play.
• Very young children are unlikely to fully understand what has happened but they will pick up and react to changes in the people who they are closest to and a shift in the mood of others around them.
• Just like adults, children can have periods of intense grief and periods of calm. One minute they can seem quite happy and the next they are inconsolable. This can be distressing to parents. Young children are able to endure strong emotions for brief periods, they alternately approach and avoid feelings so as not to be overwhelmed.
• Children may be frightened to ask questions or talk about the death for fear of upsetting others.
• Some younger children will struggle to understand the finality of death and may think the baby can come back or have their own version of what happened.
• Some children might regress to an earlier stage of development and want to go back to a bottle or soother or start bed wetting. They might become more dependent on a favourite soft toy or blanket.
• Other reactions of children may include, becoming more needy of hugs and reassurance, separation anxiety, becoming more demanding, having more temper tantrums and anger outbursts.
• Some children can become more fearful and worry about their own deaths and worry that those close to them might die too.
• Children may also worry that they caused the death of the baby.
• Some children can have difficulty concentrating, some can become withdrawn or engage in obsessive behaviours.
• Physical complaints can be common too such as, having trouble sleeping and/or nightmares, having physical complaints like headaches, stomach-ache and loss of appetite.
• Some children may ask repeat questions as a way of trying to process the news and possibly find an alternative reality.

Looking After Yourself

Although your children need your love, support and understanding, you also need time for yourself. The physical, emotional and psychological effects of loss cannot be underestimated. Again these are just suggestions, not all of them may be appropriate for you.

• It can be hard to find the energy, patience and understanding with your children when you are grieving too. If you can, it may helpful to ask a trusted family member or friend to look after them for a few hours while you have needed time alone.
• If you can, accept all offers of practical support in the aftermath, things like cooking, shopping and cleaning can be tasks that just seem impossible and too overwhelming. Trusted friends and relatives will hopefully be happy to help out.
• Grief can be exhausting, so try and get enough rest. Your body has been through a trauma and needs rest to heal.
• Don't feel you have to hide your grief from the children. Explaining how you are feeling will help them express their feelings too.
• Please take time to fully grieve, at times it will feel totally overwhelming and unbearable, and other times more bearable. Allowing grief to be, acknowledging and feeling the pain is not easy however avoiding it or numbing the grief can lead to prolonged grief.
• I found journaling the events, associated emotions and thoughts helped me to 'face' the pain. I bought a grief journal and avoided it for a period but did not want to forget the events, so I started to write. I started with just a few words and went from there.
• Please treat yourself with compassion and understanding. Self care is vitally important especially during this traumatic time.
• When you are ready, please connect with friends and family. At times you may not want to face anyone and that's ok but isolating yourself for long periods will not be helpful.
• Well meaning friends and family can make hurtful comments; I think others really struggle to know what to say, even those closest to us. Until it has happened to them, they couldn't possibly know what it is like to receive such comments; forgive their unintended insensitivity.
• There are sources of support for bereaved parents like charities, community support groups for parents in similar circumstances, online biogs, books and online support groups. Please check in your local area for these groups. In the UK, SANDS has a local support group in your area. I really didn't think it was for me but I went to a local support group and found it very supportive to connect with others who have suffered similar losses.

You will always grieve your loss but you will start to feel better in time. The excruciating intense feelings of grief will lessen, this doesn't mean that you have finished grieving or that your loss is less significant. You will never forget your baby who you never got to raise and you will always have love for them. I believe that we are all forever connected by the love and bonds which I believe endures beyond this life.
Remember, take care of yourself, accept all offers of help, take time to grieve and heal.
Connect with others.
Wishing you much comfort.

Irene

UK Support Agencies and Charities Contacts

Aching Arms
www.achingarms.co.uk
Aching Arms is a baby loss charity run by a group of bereaved parents who have experienced the pain and emptiness of leaving hospital without their baby. Their aim is to raise awareness of the impact of pregnancy and baby loss and bring some comfort to bereaved parents and their families after the loss of a baby.

ARC
www.arc.uk.org.
Support for parents who experienced a late miscarriage or loss after 24 weeks following a diagnosis of fetal anomaly (parents who continue with the pregnancy and parents who end the pregnancy.)
Helpline 0845 077 2290   Email:info@arc-uk.org

Bliss - the special care baby charity
www.bliss.org.uk
Support, advice and information to families of babies in intensive care and special care, including in situations of loss and future pregnancies.
Helpline 0808 801 0322   Email:hello@bliss.org.uk

Child Bereavement UK
www.childbereavement.org.uk
Supporting families when a baby or child dies and when a child is bereaved, including support in another pregnancy.
Freephone: 0800 0288840   Email: support@childbereavementuk.org

Cruse Bereavement Care
www.cruse.org.uk
Support, bereavement counselling and advice to children , young people and adults when someone dies.
Telephone: 0808 808 1677   Email: helpline@cruse.org.uk

Mariposa Trust/Saying Goodbye
www.mariposatrust.org
Offers support to people who have suffered baby loss in pregnancy, at birth or infancy.
Helpline: 0845 293 8027   Email: info@mariposatrust.org

Making Miracles
www .makingmiracles.org. uk
Making miracles is a baby trauma and family bereavement care charity. They offer professional support and counselling to family members including parents, siblings, and grandparents.
Telephone: 01622 735230   Email: kelly@makingmiracles.org.uk

Miscarriage Association
www .miscariageassociation.org. uk
Support and information for those affected by pregnancy loss.
Helpline: 01924 200 799   Email: info@miscarriageassociation.org.uk

Sands: Stillbirth and Neonatal Death Charity
www.sands.org. uk
Support for bereaved families, offering UK wide local support groups, online forums, helpline, booklets and other resources.
Telephone: 020 74367940/0808164 3332   Email: info@sands.org.uk

SOFT UK
www.soft.org.uk
Support for Trisomy 18, Edwards' Syndrome and Trisomy 13, Palau's Syndrome. Provide information and support to families at every stage.

Tommy's
www.tommys.org
Through clinics, research centres, pregnancy information service and support line run by the team of Tommy's midwives, they are here to support parents and families who lose a baby, experience pregnancy loss and stillbirth and premature birth.
Telephone :020 7398 3400   Email: mailbox@tommys.org

Winstons Wish
www.winstonswish.org.uk
Help and support for bereaved children and young people.
Helpline: 0845 203 0405   Email: info@winstonswish.org.uk

Some Books on the Subject of Pregnancy Loss

For children
We were having a baby and got an angel instead by Pat Schwiebert
The Baby by Joseph Hopkins
Something happened: A book for children and parents who have experienced Pregnancy Loss by Cathy Blanford.
These Precious Little People by Frankie Brunker
In the Stars by Sam Kitson & Katie Fathfull
A Star for Bobby by Helen Keenor
Our Heaven Baby: A book on miscarriage and the hope of heaven by Leah Vis
Oliver loses his little brother by Selina Langenscheid

For parents
Bearing the Unbearable: The heartbreaking path of love, loss and grief by Dr. Joanne Cacctiatore
Ask me his name: learning to live and laugh again after the loss of my baby by Eile Wright
Life after baby loss by Nicola Gaskin
Saying Goodbye by Zoe Clark- Coates
Loved Baby- Helping you grieve and cherish your child after pregnancy loss by Sarah Philpott
Empty Arms - Coping with Miscarriage , Still birth and Infant death by Sherokee Ilse and Arlene Applebaum
Empty Arms: Support for Sufferers of Miscarriage, Still birth and Tubal Pregnancy by Pam Vredevelt
Grieving the child I never knew by Kathe Wunnenberg
Empty Cradle Broken Heart: Surviving the Death of your Baby by Deborah Davis
I will carry you - The Sacred Dance of Grief and Joy by Angie Smith
A Silent Sorrow: Pregnancy Loss: Guidance and Support for you and your family by Ingrid Kohn. A
Guide for Fathers: When a baby dies by Tim Nelson.

Dear Caidain,
You were an answer to a prayer,
Another child we longed to bear.
We loved you from the start.
You fought for life while we had aching hearts.
We will remember you always as one of us,
We will remember you often, I promise.
Although we don't know why or understand why you
couldn't be
I know that God has a plan and we will meet eventually.
For now we wish you all the joys of heaven
Guide, Bless and protect us, our dearest Caidain.

Made in the USA
Las Vegas, NV
10 June 2023

73247116R00026